THE MAHABHARATA
CHILDREN'S ILLUSTRATED CLASSICS

PANDAVAS *in* EXILE

Retold by CHARU AGARWAL DHANDIA
Art KAVITA SINGH KALE   *Design* RACHITA RAKYAN

Published by
Rupa Publications India Pvt. Ltd 2020
7/16, Ansari Road, Daryaganj
New Delhi 110002

Sales centres:
Allahabad Bengaluru Chennai
Hyderabad Jaipur Kathmandu
Kolkata Mumbai

Edition copyright © Rupa Publications Pvt. Ltd 2020

All rights reserved.
No part of this publication may be reproduced, transmitted,
or stored in a retrieval system, in any form or by any means, electronic, mechanical, photocopying,
recording or otherwise,
without the prior permission of the publisher.

ISBN: 978-81-291-4976-3

First impression 2020

10 9 8 7 6 5 4 3 2 1

The moral right of the author has been asserted.

Printed at Nutech Print Services - India

This book is sold subject to the condition that it shall not, by way of trade or otherwise, be lent, resold, hired out, or otherwise circulated, without the publisher's prior consent, in any form of binding or cover other than that in which it is published.

Charu Agarwal Dhandia weaves together her two biggest passions—studying Indian classical literature and creative storytelling. She is an economist by training and works in the social development space.

Kavita Singh Kale's background as an artist and a designer enables her to draw a thin line between design following functionality and pure self-expression. This has helped her evolve as a transmedia artist. Her work includes art installations, children's books, comics, paintings and videos.

Rachita Rakyan combines over 15 years of expertise in graphic design and art direction with deep understanding of functionality and aesthetics across print, publishing, branding and digital media.

CONTENTS

KURU DYNASTY	*IV-V*
KEY CHARACTERS	*VI-VII*
PANDAVAS LEAVE INDRAPRASTHA	1
MAITREYA'S CURSE	13
DURYODHANA LEAVES FOR KAMYAKA	17
ARJUNA IN INDRAKILA	21
LORD YAMA	29
PANDAVAS IN MATSYA	39

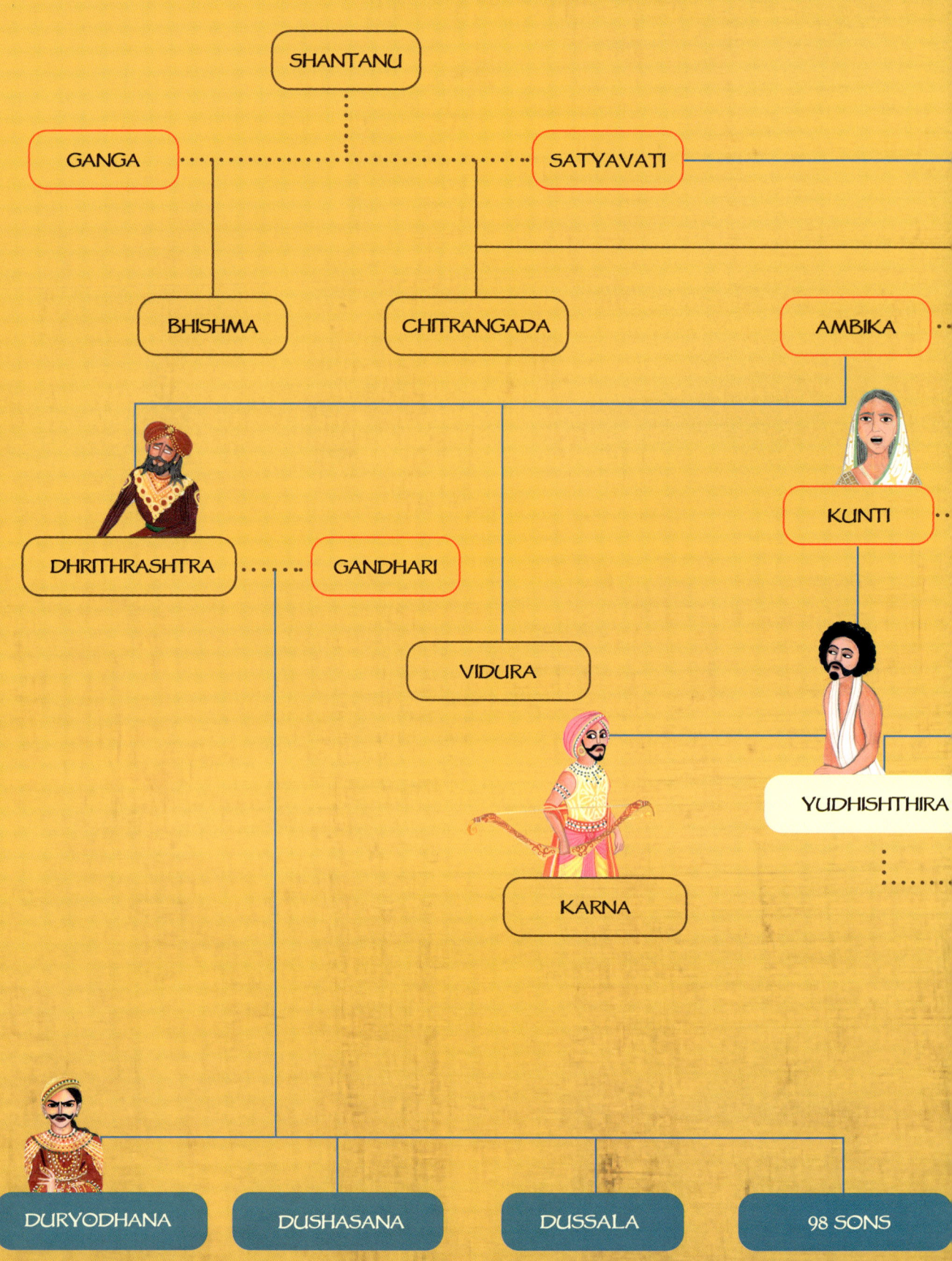

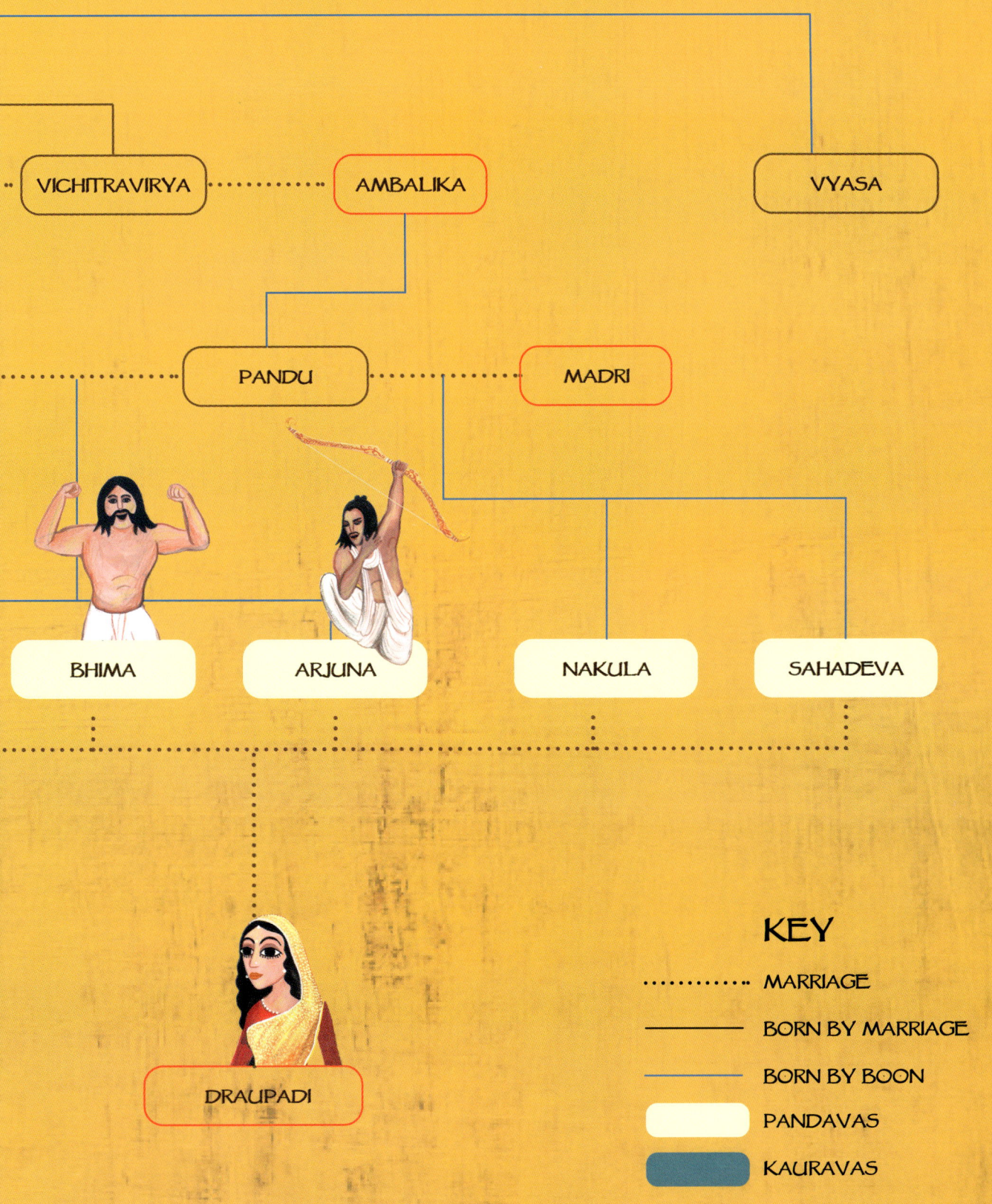

KEY CHARACTERS

DURYODHANA

Duryodhana was the eldest brother amongst the Kauravas and born to princess Gandhari as a blessing from sage Vyasa. He was very jealous of the Pandavas.

YUDHISHTHIRA

Yudhishthira was the eldest Pandava born to Kunti as a blessing from Lord Dharma. He ruled Indraprastha and later Hastinapur. Yudhishthira proved to be a great ruler and was known for his virtues of honesty, loyalty, justice, tolerance and brotherhood.

ARJUNA

Arjuna was the third of the Pandava brothers born to Kunti by the boon of Lord Indra. He was the greatest archer in the country. Arjuna was Dronacharya's favourite pupil.

VIRATA

Virata was the king of Matsya kingdom. During their exile, the Pandavas disguised themselves to stay in his court.

DRAUPADI

Draupadi was a young and beautiful girl, born from the flames of a fire yagna to King Drupada of Panchala, along with her brother Dhrishtadyumna. When Drapaudi grew up, Arjuna won her swayamvar and eventually she married all the five Pandavas.

SAGE MAITREYA

Maitreya was an old and powerful sage. He went to Hastinapur to advise Duryodhana to call the Pandavas back from their exile. But when Duryodhana showed him no respect, sage Maitreya cursed that Duryodhana would be killed by Bhima someday.

PANDAVAS LEAVE INDRAPRASTHA

Duryodhana, the eldest Kaurava, invited the Pandava brothers to Hastinapur for a game of dice. Uncle Shakuni helped him cheat and win the game. So the Pandavas had to spend the next thirteen years in exile. The Pandavas were very popular amongst the people of Hastinapur. They watched sadly as the princes and their wife Draupadi prepared to leave Hastinapur.

Draupadi's father Drupada and brother Dhrishtadyumna came to Hastinapur to bid them goodbye.

Dhrishtadyumna said angrily, 'The Kauravas have unjustly taken away everything from the Pandavas. I will take revenge on them for this!'

A few brahmins walked towards the forest with the Pandavas. Yudhishthira said to the brahmins, 'We are grateful for your love and concern for us. But this is a tough path. We do not have enough food to feed everyone. We request you to go back.'
But the brahmins refused to go back.

Soon they crossed river Ganga and it was time for dinner. But there was not enough for everyone to eat.

Yudhishthira did not know what to do. He closed his eyes and prayed to Lord Surya.

Suddenly Lord Surya appeared before him! He said, 'Yudhishthira, I am impressed by your concern for the brahmins. Do not worry, take this.'

He handed Yudhishthira a copper vessel. 'This is *Akshayapatra*, a magical vessel. This will be filled with food whenever you need it,' he said.

Yudhishthira was very happy. His problem was solved! He thanked Lord Surya and happily returned to the others. Every day, *Akshayapatra* would become full and there was enough to feed everyone. The brahmins ate first and the princes and Draupadi emptied it.

After some days, the Pandavas reached the banks of river Saraswati. The great sage Maitreya saw them living in the forest. He was furious with the Kauravas for he knew what had happened.

He left for Hastinapur to meet King Dhrithrashtra and Duryodhana. Maitreya said to Dhrithrashtra angrily, 'Duryodhana and Shakuni have cheated the Pandavas to win the game.'

When Duryodhana entered the court, Maitreya said, 'Duryodhana, you must call the Pandavas back to Hastinapur!'

Duryodhana laughed and rudely replied, 'I will never do that! I don't care about the Pandavas!'

Maitreya said, 'You are such an arrogant man. I curse you that you will be destroyed by the powerful Bhima!'

Everyone in the court requested Maitreya to take his curse back. But arrogant Duryodhana continued to laugh at him. Maitreya left the palace angrily.

DURYODHANA LEAVES FOR KAMYAKA

Duryodhana was curious to see how the Pandavas were living in the forest. One morning, he left in his chariot to meet them in the forest.

Chitrasena, a friend of the Pandavas, saw Duryodhana entering the forest. Chitrasena understood why he had come. He tried to stop Duryodhana from going into the forest. But Duryodhana did not listen. So Chitrasena held Duryodhana captive.

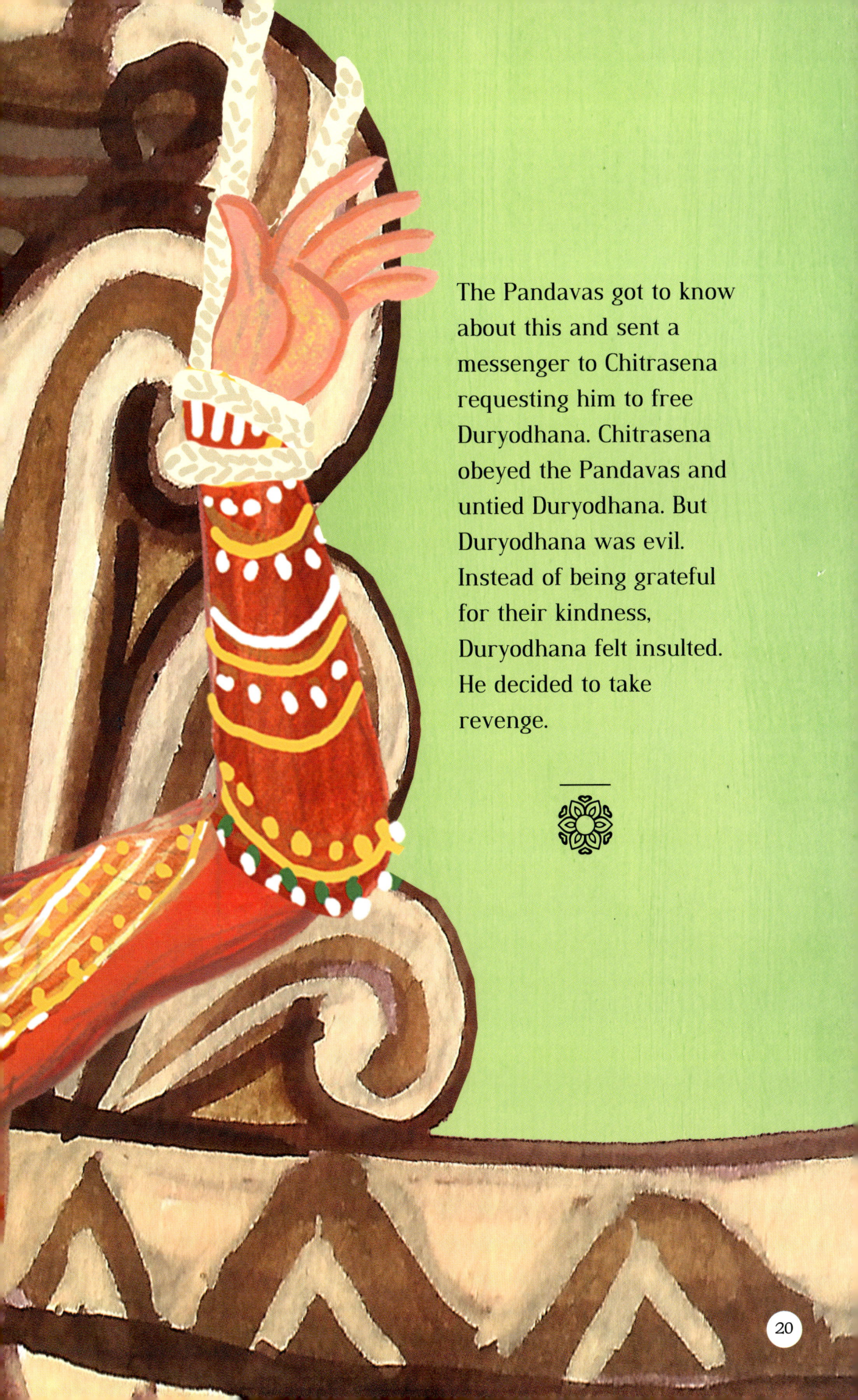

The Pandavas got to know about this and sent a messenger to Chitrasena requesting him to free Duryodhana. Chitrasena obeyed the Pandavas and untied Duryodhana. But Duryodhana was evil. Instead of being grateful for their kindness, Duryodhana felt insulted. He decided to take revenge.

ARJUNA IN INDRAKILA

One day, Yudhishthira said to Arjuna, 'We should preprare ourselves for a war with the Kauravas.'

'You should leave the forest and pray to the Gods to bless you with powerful weapons,' Yudhishthira continued.

Arjuna obeyed his brother's instructions. The next day, he left for Indrakila. He wanted to be blessed with Lord Shiva's powerful *astra*, Pasupata.

Arjuna reached Indrakila and sat on a mountain peak. He made a small clay idol of Lord Shiva and began praying. One day, he heard the sound of a wild boar. It disturbed Arjuna in his prayers. He picked up his bow and aimed at the boar. Just before he could shoot, another arrow came flying and hit the boar.

Arjuna was shocked! 'Who dares to take away my target?' he thought. It made him furious. He turned and saw a hunter standing behind him. Arjuna attacked the hunter but could not defeat him.

Arjuna prayed to Lord Shiva for help and flung a flower garland towards the clay idol. What happened next shocked Arjuna!

The garland flew and landed around the hunter's neck. The hunter was Lord Shiva himself! 'I was testing your strength and you have impressed me! Here is the Pasupata,' said Lord Shiva as he handed over the powerful *astra* to Arjuna.

Now various Gods appeared and gave their special weapons to Arjuna. He became the strongest warrior amongst all the Pandavas and Kauravas princes.

LORD YAMA

Soon the other Pandavas also reached Indrakila. One afternoon, Yudhishthira asked Sahadeva to look for some water to drink. Sahadeva walked for sometime and saw a big pond. He went near and bent to drink some water.

But before he could touch the water, a voice startled him. It said, 'You have to answer my questions before you drink!'

Sahadeva looked around and saw no one. He ignored the voice and quickly drank some water. Suddenly, he collapsed and fell on the ground.

When Sahadeva did not return for some time, the other Pandavas got worried. Yudhishthira sent Nakula to look for him.

Nakula reached the pond. Before he touched the water, he heard the same voice. 'You have to answer my questions before you drink any water!' it said.

Nakula could see nobody, so he also ignored the voice and drank the water. He too collapsed like Sahadeva. The same happened with Arjuna and Bhima. At last, Yudhishthira went in search of his brothers and reached the pond.

There, he saw his brothers lying unconscious. When he heard the voice, he did not ignore it.
'I will answer all your questions. But please return my brothers to me,' he requested the voice.

Then the voice asked Yudhishthira a hundred questions, which he answered sincerely. Soon the Pandavas came alive and the pond lit up with bright white light. A shining mount emerged from the water with a heavenly being in it.
'I am Lord Yama. Yudhishthira, you have impressed me! I advise you to go to Matsya, the kingdom of King Virata, to spend your years of exile. You will be safe there.' Saying this, he disappeared.

PANDAVAS IN MATSYA

The Pandavas followed Lord Yama's advice and left for Matsya. They disguised themselves so that no one could recognize them.

Yudhishthira became a brahmin called Kanka, Arjuna became a dancer called Brihannala and Bhima, a cook called Valala. Draupadi became the Queen's maid and called herself Sairandhri.

Meanwhile, Duryodhana and Karna were preparing to attack the kingdom of Matsya.
A huge army was formed with Duryodhana as the chief. Soon they attacked Matsya.

King Virata was worried. The Matsya army was not ready for war.

Yudhishthira, disguised as Kanka, came to King Virata and said, 'Me and my siblings Brihannala and Valala were warriors in King Yudhishthira's army in Hastinapur. We can help you fight the Kaurava army.'

King Virata was greatly relieved. He said, 'That is very generous of you! But my young son, prince Uttara does not have a charioteer for the war.'

Draupadi was listening from a corner. She came forward and said, 'Your Majesty, Brihannala is a skilled charioteer. You could send him to war as Prince Uttara's charioteer.'

King Virata readily agreed.

So Arjuna, disguised as Brihannala, drove Prince Uttara's chariot. Uttara saw Duryodhana leading the mighty Kaurava army and got very scared, He asked Arjuna to turn back, but Arjuna refused. Then Arjuna revealed that he was a prince. He said, 'Prince Uttara, I request you to drive your chariot now. I will fight Duryodhana and his army.' Uttara agreed and Arjuna attacked the Kaurava army with all his might.

Soon Duryodhana and Bhishma realized that this fearless and brave warrior could be none other than Arjuna. They understood that they would not win and decided to return to Hastinapur.

Back in the palace, King Virata got to know that Prince Uttara's charioteer was none other than Prince Arjuna! Arjuna had helped Prince Uttara fight the Kauravas. The king was very happy. He called Arjuna to his court and said, 'I am grateful to you for saving my son's life.'

Happily, Arjuna called the other Pandavas and Draupadi to the court. Then he told King Virata who they actually were. King Virata was very happy and requested all of them to live in Matsya as long as they wanted.

TITLES IN THIS SERIES

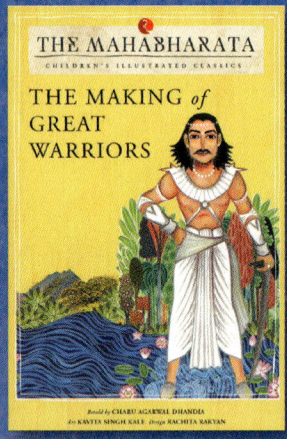
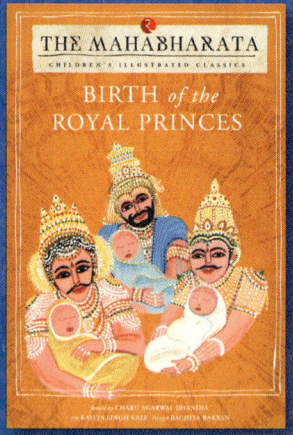
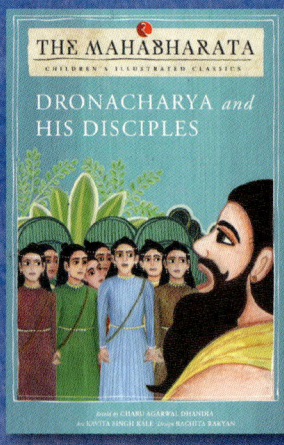
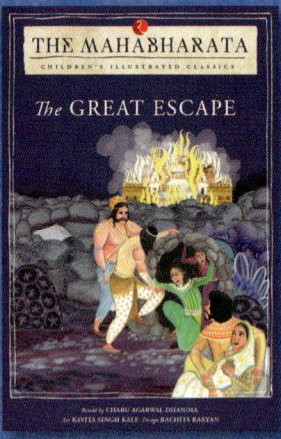
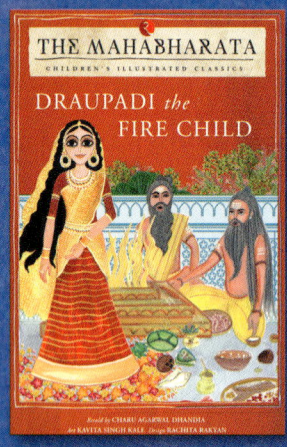
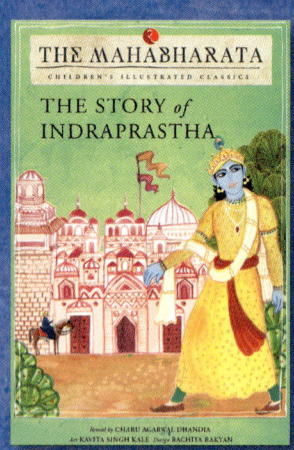
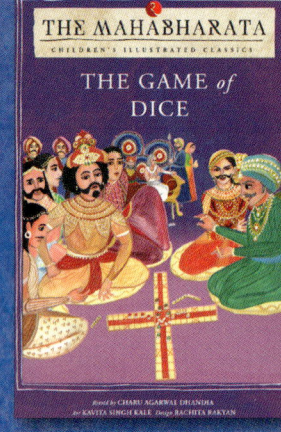
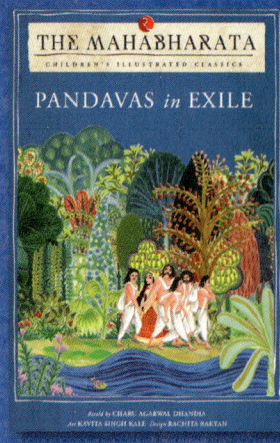
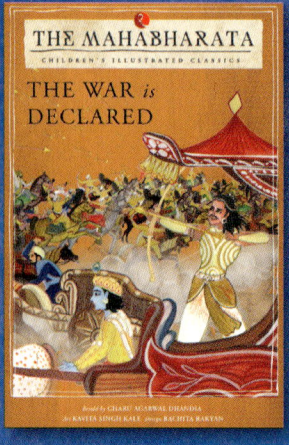